SAVITRI

LONG AGO, IN THE KINGDOM OF
MADRA RULED A KING CALLED ASVAPATI.
HE WAS A RIGHTEOUS KING.

HE HAD MANY WIVES – AS WAS THE CUSTOM IN THOSE DAYS. THE PALACE ECHOED WITH THEIR HAPPY VOICES.

BUT ASVAPATI WAS UNHAPPY. HE HAD NO CHILDREN.
WHY ARE YOU SAD, YOUR MAJESTY?
I HAVE WORSHIPPED THE GODS BUT STILL HAVE NO CHILD.

YOUR MAJESTY! I'HAVE HEARD GOD SAVITR FULFILS MANY WISHES!
SAVITR? THEN I SHALL GO TO HIS TEMPLE.

SOON A ROYAL PROCESSION WOUND ITS WAY TO THE SAVITR TEMPLE...

FROM THIS HOLY FIRE THE GOD WILL ACCEPT YOUR OFFERING!
WILL HE FULFIL MY HEART'S DESIRE?
THEN THE TEMPLE WAS BATHED IN LIGHT AND THE GOD APPEARED BEFORE THE KING.
YOU ARE PURE IN HEART! YOUR WISH WILL BE FULFILLED!

THE MONTHS PASSED. ON THE DAY OF THE CHILD'S BIRTH, THE PEOPLE GATHERED OUTSIDE THE PALACE GATES WAITING FOR THE NEWS.
ANY NEWS?
DO YOU THINK IT WILL BE A BOY?

IN THE PALACE, LATER –
GO, TELL THE KING! IT'S A GIRL.

YOUR MAJESTY! A PRINCESS HAS BEEN BORN!
AT LAST!

THE WHOLE KINGDOM REJOICED. THE KING GAVE AWAY CLOTHES AND JEWELS.

LONG LIVE OUR PRINCESS!

I SHALL CALL HER SAVITRI AFTER THE GOD SAVITR.

THE PALACE WAS FILLED WITH THE CHILD'S LAUGHTER.
YOU BRING UP A DAUGHTER AND ONE DAY SHE LEAVES FOR ANOTHER HOME!
GIRLS ARE LIKE FLOWERS! WHEREVER THEY GO, THEY MAKE THE WORLD BEAUTIFUL!

AS SHE GREW UP, SAVITRI LEARNT MUSIC, PHILOSOPHY...

...AND ASTRONOMY...
DO STARS RULE OUR FATE?

...THEN TO THE GROWING GIRL CAME THE KNOWLEDGE OF PAIN... OF SEPARATION.
FATHER! MY FRIENDS SAY A GIRL MUST MARRY AND GO AWAY! I WILL NOT GO ANYWHERE!
HA! HA! IT'S NOT TIME YET FOR THAT, MY DEAR!

BUT TIME PASSED... SAVITRI HAD GROWN TO BE A BEAUTIFUL WOMAN. ONE DAY SHE CAME TO HER FATHER.
FATHER! MAY I GO TO THE TEMPLE?
ALL ALONE? WELL, YES! YOU ARE OLD ENOUGH!

IN THE QUIET STILLNESS OF THE TEMPLE SITUATED ON A HILL TOP, SAVITRI'S HEART WAS FILLED WITH HAPPINESS.
WHY DIDN'T I COME HERE BEFORE?

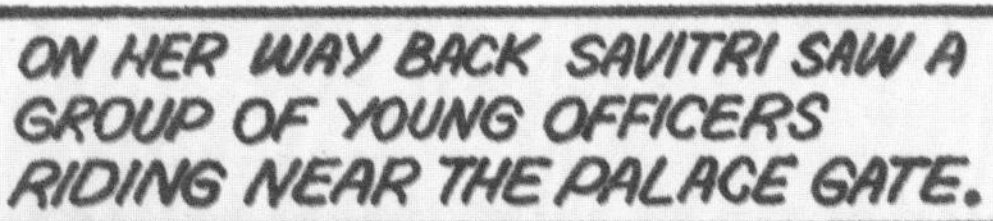
ON HER WAY BACK SAVITRI SAW A GROUP OF YOUNG OFFICERS RIDING NEAR THE PALACE GATE.

GOOD DAY, PRINCESS!

WHY DID YOU BOW YOUR HEAD TO ME?
BECAUSE YOU ARE OUR PRINCESS!

WERE SHE NOT A PRINCESS, I'D STILL BOW BEFORE ONE SO BEAUTIFUL!

SAVITRI OVERHEARD THE REMARK OF THE YOUNG OFFICER AND BLUSHED RED IN THE FACE.
SUCH BEAUTIFUL HORSES!
COME, SAVITRI, WE'RE GETTING LATE!

THE KING HAD WATCHED THE INCIDENT FROM THE PALACE WINDOW.

FATHER, I'VE BROUGHT YOU FLOWERS FROM THE TEMPLE!
WHY ARE YOU RED IN THE FACE, MY CHILD?

LOOKING AT THE RECEDING FIGURE OF HIS DAUGHTER, THE KING REALISED HOW BEAUTIFUL SHE HAD BECOME.
OH! IT'S THE SUN OUTSIDE!
I MUST FIND A HUSBAND FOR HER.

NEWS OF SAVITRI'S BEAUTY AND LEARNING HAD REACHED OTHER ROYAL COURTS.
THE MADRA KING'S DAUGHTER IS ELIGIBLE FOR MARRIAGE!
LOOK AT MY SONS! HOW CAN YOU THINK OF SUCH A MATCH?

ANOTHER KING'S COURT—
NO, NOT MY SON! A LEARNED WOMAN LIKE HER DESERVES SOMEONE BETTER!

IT WAS THE SAME STORY EVERYWHERE...
THE PRINCE HAS GROWN UP. SHALL WE APPROACH THE KING OF MADRA?
YOU MEAN SAVITRI? NO, I DON'T THINK WE CAN DO HER HONOUR!

...NO ONE DARED ASK FOR SAVITRI'S HAND.
HAVE WE RECEIVED ANY PROPOSALS FOR SAVITRI?
NO, YOUR MAJESTY!

THE COURT JESTER CAME OUT WITH ANOTHER IDEA...
WHY NOT LET HER CHOOSE HERSELF?
ARE YOU JOKING?

THE KING LIKED THE IDEA. HE CALLED SAVITRI TO HIS ROOM. SAVITRI WAS RELUCTANT.

I DON'T WISH TO MARRY! WHY DO YOU WANT TO SEND ME AWAY?

IT IS SAID, A FATHER, WHO DOES NOT GIVE HIS DAUGHTER IN MARRIAGE, IS A SINNER.

ALL RIGHT, FATHER! I SHALL DO WHAT YOU SAY.

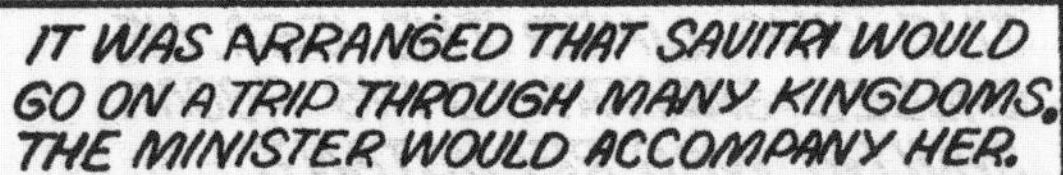
IT WAS ARRANGED THAT SAVITRI WOULD GO ON A TRIP THROUGH MANY KINGDOMS. THE MINISTER WOULD ACCOMPANY HER.

LOOK FOR A HUSBAND WHO WILL BE YOUR EQUAL.

SAVITRI WAS THRILLED WITH THE JOURNEY— SHE WOULD VISIT SO MANY HOLY PLACES.

WHILE PASSING THROUGH A FOREST, THEY SAW A YOUNG HERMIT WALKING BY THE SIDE OF THE ROAD.

SAVITRI'S EYES FELL ON THE YOUNG MAN'S FACE AND SHE FELT A STRANGE EMOTION.
SO YOUNG, AND YET A HERMIT?

THE FACE WAS IMPRINTED ON HER MEMORY.
TOMORROW WE SHALL BE THE GUESTS OF THE KING OF VARANASI!

AT VARANASI_
MY SONS ARE BRAVE AND STRONG! YOU MAY MAKE YOUR CHOICE, MY CHILD.

FOR SAVITRI, A CHANCE MEETING HAD DIMMED THE REST OF THE WORLD.
HAVE YOU MADE YOUR CHOICE?
NO! LET'S GO BACK HOME!

WHAT KIND OF A MAN DO YOU WANT FOR A HUSBAND?
HOW CAN I TELL HIM? I DON'T EVEN KNOW HIS NAME!

THE CHARIOT PASSED THROUGH THE FOREST AGAIN. SAVITRI SENSED THAT SHE WOULD MEET HIM AGAIN.
I AM THIRSTY! CAN WE STOP FOR SOME WATER?
I SEE A COTTAGE THERE! I'LL GO AND SEE!

SOON SHE WAS STARTLED BY A WARM YOUTHFUL VOICE...
MAY I GIVE SOME WATER TO THE PRINCESS?
YES, IT'S HE! BUT HE IS A HERMIT! HOW CAN I...?

SAVITRI KNEW SHE HAD TO KNOW THE TRUTH! SHE COULD NOT GO AWAY.
PLEASE STOP! FIND OUT WHO HE IS! EVERYTHING!
ALL RIGHT! I'LL GO!

SOON THE MINISTER RETURNED.
HE IS NO HERMIT! HIS NAME IS SATYAVAN, SON OF AN EXILED KING. BUT, IS HE YOUR CHOICE?
YES!

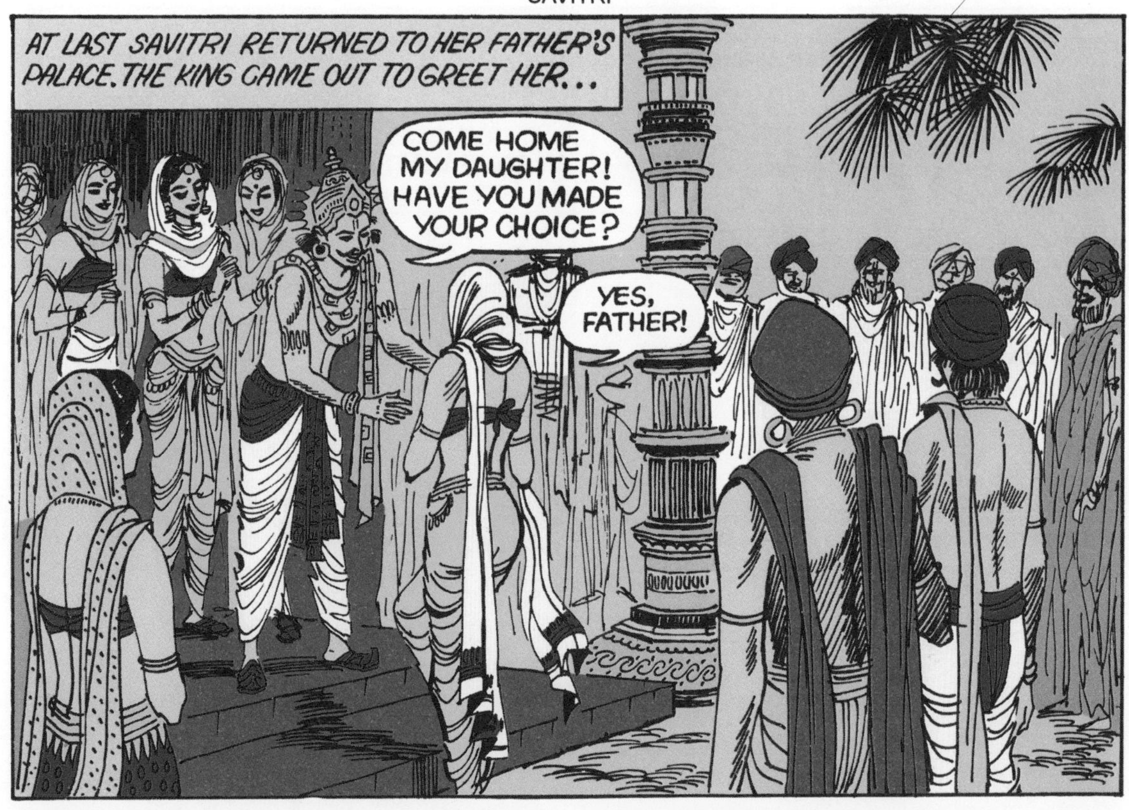
AT LAST SAVITRI RETURNED TO HER FATHER'S PALACE. THE KING CAME OUT TO GREET HER...
COME HOME MY DAUGHTER! HAVE YOU MADE YOUR CHOICE?
YES, FATHER!

BUT SAVITRI WAS SOON OVERCOME WITH EMBARRASSMENT... SHE COULD NOT SPEAK...
WHY DO YOU BLUSH, MY DEAR?
SHE HAS CHOSEN SATYAVAN! HE LIVES IN THE FOREST.
IN THE FOREST?

...BUT THE CONVERSATION WAS SOON INTERRUPTED.
YOUR MAJESTY! SAGE NARADA SEEKS YOUR AUDIENCE!
OH! I MUST GO AND WELCOME HIM!

WHAT IS THIS LITTLE CONFERENCE ABOUT?
MY DAUGHTER HAS CHOSEN A POOR MAN FOR HER HUSBAND! HIS NAME IS SATYAVAN!

SATYAVAN?
WHY DID SHE HAVE TO CHOOSE HIM?

THE KING HAD SEEN THE LOOK OF SADNESS IN NARADA'S EYES.
DO YOU KNOW HIM?
YES! HIS FATHER DYUMATSENA WAS KING OF SALVA! AFTER HE BECAME BLIND, HE LOST HIS KINGDOM!

THEN WHY ARE YOU SILENT? IS IT BECAUSE THEY LIVE IN THE FOREST NOW?
NO, NOT THAT!
HOW CAN I TELL HIM THE REAL REASON!

ASVAPATI KEPT ON ASKING THE SAGE.
IS HE NOT NOBLE? IS HE NOT BRAVE?
HE IS THE NOBLEST AND BRAVEST OF ALL!

FINALLY NARADA HAD TO COME OUT WITH THE TRUTH.
HE IS DESTINED TO DIE EXACTLY ONE YEAR FROM TODAY.

THAT MEANS MY CHILD WILL BE A WIDOW IN A YEAR?
YES! IF SHE MARRIES HIM!

ASVAPATI WAS VERY UPSET. HE CALLED SAVITRI.
MY CHILD! YOU CANNOT MARRY SATYAVAN! HE IS GOING TO DIE SOON!

BUT FATHER! I'VE ALREADY CHOSEN HIM WITH MY HEART! HOW COULD I MARRY ANYONE ELSE?

AT LAST, ASVAPATI HAD TO GIVE IN.
YOUR DAUGHTER HAS MADE A BRAVE CHOICE! PLEASE ACCEPT IT!
YES! I'LL ACCEPT IT!

ONE DAY SOON AFTER, A BRIDAL PROCESSION REACHED THE FOREST... THE HERMITS CAME FORWARD TO RECEIVE AND WELCOME THEM.

AT FIRST, DYUMATSENA WAS HESITANT.

HER FRIENDS DRESSED SAVITRI BEAUTIFULLY.

CHANTING THE SACRED MANTRA OF MARRIAGE, ASVAPATI GAVE AWAY HIS DAUGHTER TO SATYAVAN.

THE BRIDE AND GROOM WALKED AROUND THE SACRED FIRE SEVEN TIMES. THEY WERE MARRIED NOW.

THEN IT WAS TIME FOR FAREWELL.

AS SOON AS HER PARENTS LEFT, SAVITRI TOOK OFF ALL HER JEWELS AND CLOTHED HERSELF IN CLOTHES OF BARK.

SATYAVAN TOOK OUT A BEAUTIFUL RING HE HAD KEPT FOR HER.

SAVITRI WAS EXTREMELY DEVOTED TO HER PARENTS-IN-LAW! SHE LOOKED AFTER THEM LIKE A DUTIFUL DAUGHTER.
IT'S LATE, MY CHILD! YOU MUST GO TO BED!
IS THERE ANYTHING ELSE I CAN DO?

AS THE DAYS PASSED, A SECRET AGONY GREW WITHIN HER HEART.
WHAT DAY IS IT TODAY, MOTHER?
THE EIGHTH DAY AFTER THE NEW MOON!
ONLY SIXTY DAYS MORE!

AT LAST, THE YEAR WENT BY. THREE DAYS BEFORE THE FATE-FUL DAY, SAVITRI BEGAN FASTING.
BUT, MY CHILD! THIS IS TOO HARD A PENANCE!
PLEASE DO NOT WORRY, FATHER! I CAN DO IT!

ON THE LAST NIGHT SHE COULD NOT SLEEP. ONLY ONE THOUGHT KEPT ON HAUNTING HER.
TOMORROW MY HUSBAND IS FATED TO DIE! WHAT SHALL I DO?

IN THE MORNING...
PLEASE LET ME GO WITH YOU TODAY.
WHY SAVITRI?

I JUST WANT TO GO!
ALL RIGHT, COME WITH ME!

HER SMILING FACE HID THE AGONY IN HER HEART. SATYAVAN WAS HAPPY...
BUT YOU MUST WEAR YOUR ANKLETS! I WANT TO HEAR YOUR FOOTSTEPS!

IN THE FOREST, SAVITRI'S HEART WAS FULL OF ANGUISH.
THE WORLD IS BEAUTIFUL! BUT LIFE IS TOO SHORT TO APPRECIATE EVERYTHING!
SAVITRI! WHY DO YOU HAVE SUCH SAD THOUGHTS?

EVERY SECOND, HER HEART BEATS BECAME LOUDER! EVERY BLADE OF GRASS SMELLED OF LURKING DEATH.
AREN'T YOU TIRED? DO YOU WISH TO REST A WHILE?
NO SAVITRI! WITH YOU, I FEEL NO WEARINESS!

WILL YOU PLUCK SOME FRUIT? I HAVE TO CUT BRANCHES FOR FIREWOOD!
YES, I WILL!

SUDDENLY, SATYAVAN'S BODY WAS BATHED IN PERSPIRATION... THEN A TERRIBLE PAIN SHOT THROUGH HIS LIMBS.
SAVITRI!
OH! NO!

SAVITRI RAN TOWARDS HER HUSBAND...
SAVITRI, MY LIMBS ARE LOSING ALL SENSATION! LET ME SLEEP FOR A WHILE!

SOON, SATYAVAN'S BODY BECAME STILL.
SO THIS IS THE END?

THE FOREST AROUND HER HAD DARKENED... A HEAVY STILLNESS FILLED THE AIR... SAVITRI LIFTED HER HEAD AND SAW A DARK FIGURE CLAD IN RED, A CROWN SHINING ON HIS HEAD.

SAVITRI WAS TROUBLED, BUT SHE FELT NO FEAR. SHE WANTED TO SPEAK TO HIM...
WHO ARE YOU?
HAVEN'T YOU GUESSED? I AM YAMA, GOD OF DEATH. I'VE COME FOR SATYAVAN'S SOUL!

MY LORD! I'VE HEARD, YOUR ASSISTANTS DO THIS JOB. WHY HAVE YOU COME YOURSELF?
SATYAVAN WAS NO ORDINARY PERSON. HE WAS PURE. THAT'S WHY I HAVE COME!

YAMA TOOK OUT A SMALL NOOSE. HE SLIPPED IT AROUND SATYAVAN'S BODY AND STARTED BACK.

SAVITRI SAW THAT SATYAVAN'S FACE HAD ASSUMED THE STILLNESS OF A A CORPSE.
MY BELOVED HUSBAND IS DEAD! I HAVE NOTHING LEFT NOW IN LIFE! LET ME FOLLOW LORD YAMA!

SAVITRI FOLLOWED YAMA FROM A DISTANCE! THE TALL SOFT GRASS OF THE FOREST MUFFLED THE SOUND OF HER ANKLETS.

SOON THEY CAME UPON A STREAM. HERE TOO THE WATER SOFTENED THE SOUND OF HER FOOTSTEPS.

ON THE HARD GROUND, HER ANKLETS FILLED THE AIR WITH A MOURNFUL SOUND...

...WHICH SOON REACHED YAMA'S EARS! THE GOD OF DEATH PAUSED TO LISTEN TO THE STRANGE SOUND.

WHY ARE YOU FOLLOWING ME?
WHERE MY HUSBAND GOES, I TOO MUST GO.

YOUR HUSBAND IS DEAD! YOU MUST GO BACK!
NOT UNLESS HE GETS HIS LIFE BACK!

YOU ARE ASKING FOR THE IMPOSSIBLE! BUT FIRST, TELL ME WHY I SHOULD HELP YOU.
THERE WAS A TWINKLE OF AMUSEMENT IN YAMA'S EYES!

IT IS SAID, WALKING SEVEN STEPS TOGETHER, MAKES FRIENDS. I'VE WALKED MORE THAN SEVEN STEPS WITH YOU!

EVEN THE GOD OF DEATH WAS THRILLED WITH SAVITRI'S REPLY.
YOU ARE WISE! ASK FOR ANY BOON FROM ME EXCEPT FOR YOUR DEAD HUSBAND'S LIFE!
PLEASE GIVE MY FATHER-IN-LAW HIS SIGHT AND HIS KINGDOM.

SAVITRI KNEW SHE COULD NOT ASK FOR SATYAVAN'S LIFE DIRECTLY! BUT SHE FOUND A WAY!

YAMA STARTED TO GO! AFTER A FEW STEPS HE TURNED TO HAVE A LAST GLIMPSE OF SAVITRI.

IN GREAT JOY, SAVITRI RAN BACK TO WHERE SATYAVAN LAY IN THE FOREST.

HE WAS LYING THERE AS SHE HAD LEFT HIM, STILL, MOTIONLESS. SAVITRI HAD A DOUBT.
IS HE REALLY ALIVE? WHY CAN'T I SEE HIM BREATHE?

SAVITRI KNEW THAT A POLISHED STONE BECOMES MISTY WITH A MAN'S BREATH. SHE TOOK OFF HER RING AND HELD IT NEAR HIS NOSE.
OH! HE IS ALIVE! HE IS ALIVE!

SATYAVAN SOON OPENED HIS EYES.
HOW LONG HAVE I BEEN SLEEPING?

THE HAPPY COUPLE STARTED FOR THEIR HOME! SAVITRI'S HEART WAS FILLED WITH HAPPINESS.
A HUNDRED SONS, HE SAID!

MEANWHILE... DYUMATSENA HAD GOT BACK HIS SIGHT.
WHY ARE YOU LOOKING AT ME LIKE THAT ?
BECAUSE I CAN SEE YOU! IT'S A MIRACLE! MY WIFE!

BUT WHERE IS MY SON, SATYAVAN ? WHERE IS SAVITRI ? THEY SHOULD HAVE COME BACK BY NOW.

AS THE WORRIED DYUMATSENA STEPPED OUTSIDE, HE SAW A STORM CLOUD AT THE EDGE OF THE FOREST.
IS THAT A STORM APPROACHING?
NO, IT LOOKS LIKE HORSE-MEN TO ME!

THE HORSEMEN SOON ARRIVED! DYUMATSENA RECOGNISED THEM. THEY CAME FROM HIS LOST KINGDOM.
YOUR MAJESTY! THE ENEMIES HAVE BEEN DEFEATED! WE HAVE COME TO TAKE YOU BACK.
ANOTHER MIRACLE!

BUT WE MUST LOOK FOR MY SON AND HIS WIFE !
LET'S SPREAD OUT IN THE FOREST.

THE SEARCHERS DID NOT HAVE TO GO VERY FAR.
SATYAVAN ! SAVITRI! YOU HAVE COME AT LAST!
FATHER! WHAT DOES THIS MEAN?

SAVITRI! YOU CAME TO A POOR HOME! NOW YOU SHALL SIT ON A THRONE! AND YOUR SONS WILL BE PRINCES!
JUST AS LORD YAMA SAID!

THE EXILES STARTED FOR THEIR KINGDOM.
IT WAS A JOYOUS JOURNEY FOR ALL.

It was in 1967 that the first Amar Chitra Katha comic rolled off the presses, changing story-telling for children across India forever.

Five decades and more than 400 books later, we are still sharing stories from India's rich heritage, primarily because of the love and support shown by readers like yourself.

So, from us to you, here's a big

THANK YOU!